Sam's t with words

A story about a boy with dyslexia

Lorna Miles

Illustrations by Rachel Fuller

Published by
British Association for Adoption & Fostering
(BAAF)
Saffron House
6-10 Kirby Street
London EC1N 8TS
www.baaf.org.uk

Charity registration 275689 (England and Wales)
and SC039337 (Scotland)

British Library Cataloguing in Publication Data
A catalogue record for this book is available from
the British Library

ISBN 978 1 910039 08 3

Project management by Michelle Bell, Publications
Department, BAAF
Designed and typeset by Fravashi Aga
Printed in Great Britain by the Lavenham Press
Trade distribution by Turnaround Publisher Services,
Unit 3, Olympia Trading Estate, Coburg Road, London
N22 6TZ

BAAF is the leading UK-wide membership organisation
for all those concerned with adoption, fostering and
child care issues.

Acknowledgements

Thank you to all the dyslexics in my life who found the courage to share their experiences with me.

The author

Lorna Miles is an adopter and foster carer who has written/contributed to several BAAF publications about the challenges that parenting fostered and adopted children can bring (*Holding on and hanging in*, 2010, *Parenting a child with dyslexia*, 2012 and *Parenting a child with emotional and behavioural difficulties*, 2012). She is also involved in running workshops and training for foster carers. This is her first children's book which she was delighted to write as the impact that undiagnosed dyslexia can have on children's lives is something she has witnessed first-hand many times.

The illustrator

Since graduating from Brighton Art College in 1996, Rachel Fuller has produced artwork for a range of magazines, design groups and advertising agencies. She is, however, predominantly known for her work in children's books. Rachel develops her own ideas, often in the form of novelty and interactive packages for young children. She also enjoys illustrating picture books, educational material and teen fiction. She has illustrated a number of books for BAAF, including *Morris and the bundle of worries*, *Elfa and the box of memories* and *A safe place for Rufus*.

The series editor

The editor of this series, Hedi Argent, is an established author/editor for BAAF. Her books cover a wide range of family placement topics; she has written several guides and a story book for young children.

Other books in this series

My brother Booh has ADHD – A story about a boy with Attention Deficit Hyperactivity Disorder

Oli and the pink bicycle – A story about a girl born with Foetal Alcohol Syndrome

Why can't I be good? – A story about an adopted girl with behaviour problems

This is a story about a boy called Sam who has dyslexia and a girl called Rebecca who has problems keeping up with her friends at school. If you have difficulty reading and writing, or you know someone who does, you may find Sam's story helpful. Even if you can read it yourself, you may want to ask an adult to read the story with you.

You may find that lots of the things that happen to Sam, or Rebecca, have happened, or are happening, to you. After you have read Sam's story you may have lots of questions about dyslexia. There is a question and answer section at the back of this book with useful information about some of the things you may want to know about dyslexia. Of course, if you have more questions you can ask the adult reading the book with you, your parent, carer, social worker or teacher.

★

'Blah, blah, blah...' Sam could hear Miss Thomas's voice in the background but he wasn't listening to what she was saying. He had already heard the word "write" and he was in such a panic that he just couldn't concentrate on the rest of the instructions. But then even if he did he would probably forget what she had said anyway!

It was Sam's first day at Brook Hill Junior School and so far everyone seemed nice, but he was really worried that once they found out that he couldn't read or write properly everything would change.

★

Sam was fostered and had moved to Kitty and Paul Rogers's house during the school holidays. They told him that he wouldn't be moving again, they were going to be his permanent foster family, but Sam wasn't sure he believed that. He had already lived with four foster families and thought that once Kitty and Paul found out how "thick" he was they wouldn't want him any more. He did hope that he could stay with them because each time he moved to a new family he also had to move school; he just wanted to settle down, be part of a family and make friends.

He decided that it was really important to keep his troubles with reading, writing and spelling a secret and then everything would be OK.

Suddenly Sam was aware that Miss Thomas was standing beside him. 'Are you alright Sam? You haven't started your work yet. Do you understand what you are doing?'

'Yes Miss, but I need to go to the toilet. My

★

tummy hurts. It's really bad.'

'OK, off you go then, but in future try and go during break times if you can.'

As Sam got up to leave the classroom he noticed that a girl on the next table was looking at him. She smiled and waved. 'Oh no, how embarrassing,' thought Sam. The girl had a teaching assistant sitting next to her and only really, really "thick" people had one of those. He couldn't be her friend because people might think he was like her. Sam looked the other way and hurried off to the toilet.

He stayed in the toilet until the bell rang. 'Phew, that's a relief,' he thought. 'Day one is nearly over and my secret is still safe.'

★

By the end of his first week at Brook Hill Sam was feeling very pleased with himself: so far he had managed to make sure no one discovered his secret by finding lots of ways not to do any reading or writing. He kept breaking the lead in his pencil, or the ink mysteriously ran out in his pen. He spent ages looking for his rubber or accidently ripped the paper and had to start again. He even came up with a really clever plan to trick Miss Thomas into thinking he was writing.

He wrote groups of random letters on the page with spaces in between so that it looked like words. "Dujcax nof axfe kjkilded coaser

★

mafeds and kingver is..." He could manage
some of the smaller words like "is", "it" and
"the", though sometimes he got the letters in
the wrong order. He hoped Miss Thomas would
notice these little words when she looked over
his shoulder to see how he was getting on,
and not the other nonsense he had written.
But how long could he go on tricking everyone
like this? How long would it be before they
found out?

Something else was worrying him too: the
pesky girl who had waved to him on his first
day kept following him around, determined to
be his friend. She seemed to have some trouble
with her legs and couldn't walk very fast so
he had managed to get away without actually
having to talk to her, but everywhere he went
she was there, looking at him and waving.
Sam felt a bit mean avoiding her like this. She
didn't seem to have many friends and some of

★

the older boys teased her in the playground. She spoke quite slowly and seemed to have trouble saying some words and he had noticed one or two of the children in his class laughing behind their hands when she tried to answer a question. Sam knew how it felt not to have any friends because that had happened to him in his previous school – but being her friend was just too big a risk to take.

By the following week Sam had started to make some friends; a few of them knew he was fostered, but that didn't seem to worry them. They asked why he didn't live with his parents, how long he was staying and that kind of thing, but Kitty and Paul had helped him to practise what to say about that, so it hadn't been too much of a problem. Miss Thomas had said what a fantastic artist he was and had showed one of his pictures to the whole school in assembly. If he could only make sure that no one found out his secret about reading, spelling and writing, it really did seem like he could settle down and be happy here. But

★

keeping his secret was becoming more and
more difficult.

'Sam, will you stop daydreaming please. I
asked you to get into pairs and start work on
your script for the play...Rebecca hasn't got a
partner, you can work with her.'

Sam put his head on the table.
This couldn't be happening. It
was her – Rebecca was the girl
he had been avoiding. Before he
could think of an excuse, Miss Thomas
had guided him across to where Rebecca
was sitting, pulled out a chair and asked him
to sit down.

Rebecca

Rebecca, as usual, had a huge smile on
her face and looked really pleased that she
was going to be working with Sam, but he was
filled with horror. That was, until Mrs Spencer,
the teaching assistant who helped Rebecca,
came and sat at the table too. Sam was really
good at making up stories and had some great

★

ideas for the play. He had seen Mrs Spencer
help Rebecca with her writing, so if he came
up with the ideas and she wrote them down,
everything would be alright.

'I've got some great ideas…' he started to say,
but Mrs Spencer interrupted him.

'Sam, write your ideas down and Rebecca can
write hers down too, and then we can have a
chat and decide which ones you want to use.'

Sam started to feel sick. How was he going to
cover up with Mrs Spencer sitting right beside
him? 'I haven't got anything to write with
Miss. Shall I just tell you my ideas, and you
can write them down?'

'No, Mrs Spencer can't do your writing, she
has to help me with mine,' Rebecca said before
Mrs Spencer could reply. 'I've got Global
Developmental Delay so I get help. Here you
are. You can borrow one of my pencils.'

★

Sam had no idea what developmental delay meant but he did know that global meant all around the world. 'Wow...all around the world!' he thought. 'If Rebecca had been all around the world her family must be really rich. Perhaps she might be a good friend to have after all?' But he couldn't think about that now. Right now he needed to think how to stop Mrs Spencer finding out about his secret.

He sat and stared and stared at the paper in front of him. He knew what he wanted to write, but he couldn't remember the letters he needed or how to form them on the page. He put the pencil to the paper to start writing but his mind just went blank and he was beginning to panic. The backs of his eyes were starting to feel prickly, like he was going to cry. His tummy was turning somersaults and he was all angry inside. He could feel his hands making fists and he couldn't think straight. Suddenly his foot kicked out and sent the chair opposite him flying across the classroom.

★

'Sam Simpson, what are you doing?' Miss Thomas asked.

'Sorry Miss, my foot slipped. I'll go and pick it up.'

'Thank you, then get on with your work please. I will speak to you at break time.'

Sam spent ages picking the chair up and making sure it was put back exactly where it was before. On the way back to sit down he made sure that all the other empty chairs were straight too. By the time he got back to his seat Rebecca had finished making her list of ideas and Mrs Spencer asked Sam to just talk about his ideas to save time. Phew...he had got away with it again!

★

As the term went on, it became harder and harder for Sam to keep his secret and he was losing his temper more often as his worries got bigger and bigger. Some of the children who had been his friends started to avoid him and didn't want to play with him any more. Kitty and Miss Thomas were getting cross, not only because he kept losing his temper, but because he was always losing or forgetting things. Every day Kitty would remind him about what he had to take to school, but even if he had all the things he needed when she dropped him at the gates, they never seemed to arrive in the classroom with him. Only yesterday he had lost his

★

games kit and the caretaker had found it under the hedge in the playground. Sam had no idea how it got there – or did he remember putting it down when he tried to play with his friends?

One afternoon, when Kitty collected him from school, the moment Sam had been dreading finally came. She told him that there was going to be a meeting at school the next day. Kitty would be there as well as Miss Thomas and Sam's social worker, and even the headmaster. Sam knew about meetings. There had been meetings in the past and after them he had moved to a new foster home and sometimes to a new school. Sam was sure this would happen again. If only he could learn to read and write, then perhaps everything would be OK.

That night Sam sat in bed staring and staring at the pages of one of his books. Perhaps if he stayed up all night and kept trying and trying he would learn how to read before the morning. But try as he might, every time he looked at the page all he could see was a

★

jumble of letters – "pohs eht tsap. nwot eht
fo tuO. Teerts eht fo tuO. Tnew ew yawA..."
Sometimes it seemed as if they were dancing
on the page, or worse still, jumping up and
down. Perhaps they were laughing at him?

Sam tried sounding the letters out ..."b". What
did that letter sound like? Which letter was it?
"d" and "b" were so confusing. Sam's eyes kept
on trying to shut as he got more and more tired,
but he was no closer to being able to read.

The next morning Sam could hardly eat
any breakfast because he felt really sick. He
dragged behind on the way to school and
when Kitty said goodbye to him he went and
sat in a corner of the playground by himself.

'Are you alright Sam? You look really sad,' said
a voice beside him. He looked up and Rebecca
was standing there. He had got to know

★

Rebecca better because they had been working on the play together, and he was really getting to like her. The more he talked to her the easier he found it to understand what she was saying; if he spoke slowly and clearly she could understand him perfectly too. Her walking was a bit slow and wonky and she had to do special exercises every day to try and make her legs stronger, but other than in games that wasn't really a problem. She was one of the best swimmers in the class because she went swimming nearly every day after school, to help make the muscles in her legs stronger. Sam had been to her house to play a few times, but her family didn't seem to be rich; he wanted to ask her about going global and travelling all around the world, but not now. He really didn't want to talk at all. But as he started to say that it was nothing, two big tears rolled down his cheeks. 'I'm leaving,' Sam sobbed. 'I'm leaving Kitty and Paul's and I'm leaving this school.'

'No, you can't go,' cried Rebecca, 'you're my very best friend. I haven't had a best friend

★

before. You can't go!'

Sam hadn't had a best friend before either; what Rebecca said just made the situation worse. Perhaps he should go now, run away and get it over and done with. But before Sam could make a dash for it the bell rang for the start of lessons.

The morning went so slowly. Sam didn't see Rebecca at lunchtime because she was having a session with a speech therapist to help her with her talking. Sam felt sad and alone.

Just after lunch the school secretary came and called Sam out of the classroom to join the meeting. He walked into the room feeling sick and shaky but everyone was smiling at him. What was going on?

'Come and sit down Sam,' Kitty said in a kind voice. She put her arm around his shoulders and gave him a gentle squeeze. 'Don't look so worried, you're not in trouble.'

★

'We just wanted to talk to you about a problem you seem to be having with your reading and writing,' said the headmaster. 'Have you heard of something called dyslexia?'

Sam hadn't, but he was feeling confused and he wanted to hear more. They were talking about his secret but everyone was still looking happy. They hadn't mentioned his angry behaviour, told him off or, worse still, told him he was moving. He shook his head because he didn't know what to say.

The headmaster carried on talking. 'Dyslexia is a difficulty with words. It means that you can find it hard to read, write and spell, to concentrate and to remember things. But it doesn't mean that you are silly. Lots of very clever people are dyslexic.'

'Sam, it is really important that you understand that having dyslexia doesn't mean that you aren't clever,' said Kitty.

★

Miss Thomas explained. 'If you do have dyslexia, there are lots of ways we can help you. You can have extra help with reading, writing and spelling; we can let you use the computer for some of your work and we can help you to find ways to remember things better and not keep losing things.' Everyone, including Sam, laughed at that!

By the time Sam returned to the classroom, he had been told lots of things about dyslexia and how he could find out if he had it. Funnily enough, knowing he might have a problem with a name and that he wasn't just "thick" made him feel much better. 'It is strange,' he thought, 'how I can be happy about finding out

★

I really do have a problem.' He couldn't wait to tell Rebecca his news and that he wouldn't be leaving after all.

Now Sam didn't feel so worried about literacy in class and lost his temper less often. Miss Thomas kept an eye on him, and sometimes she let him sit with Rebecca so that Mrs Spencer could help him with his writing too. She also stopped being cross when he forgot or lost things, and Sam started to feel much better about himself.

★

4

Over the next few weeks Sam met different people who would help him find out if he did have dyslexia or not. Then finally, he had to have an assessment with an educational psychologist, a special person who understands how children learn. Having an assessment sounded scary but Kitty and Miss Thomas both reassured him that the psychologist, Mr Burns, would just talk to him about school, ask him to do things like jigsaw puzzles, fill in missing words and try to do some reading and spelling. But none of it

★

was a test; it was just to find out how his brain worked so they could make sure he got the right help.

Sam was still feeling very anxious when the day of the assessment finally arrived. He was really pleased when Rebecca rang him before she went to school to wish him good luck. She said that she had needed lots of assessments with a special children's doctor called a paediatrician, a speech and language therapist, a physiotherapist and an occupational therapist because of all her disabilities, and there was nothing to worry about. In fact some of the assessments had been good fun and involved playing games with a ball, balancing and doing puzzles.

'Phew,' thought Sam, 'at least I haven't got to see all those people. Poor Rebecca.'

When Sam arrived at Mr Burns's office with Kitty, he felt like someone had tied all his insides into a great big knot, but once he

★

went in he was surprised how nice it was.
There were lots of things to play with while
he was waiting and it seemed like no time
at all before Mr Burns called him and Kitty
into another room for the assessment. Sam
immediately noticed lots of pictures of famous
people around the room. Mr Burns saw him
looking at them and told him that they were
all people who had dyslexia – Roald Dahl the
author, Leonardo da Vinci and Pablo Picasso,
both famous artists, Prince Harry, Benjamin
Zephaniah the children's poet, Walt Disney the
film producer, Steve Jobs the founder of Apple
and Jamie Oliver the chef. Sam thought how
nasty he had been, thinking that people who
needed help were "thick". Now he could see
that wasn't true at all. 'Wow, perhaps I will be
famous one day!' he thought.

Jamie Oliver

★

Mr Burns explained that the assessment would help them to find out what Sam was good at and what he wasn't so good at. It would also give really important information about his special learning needs and the best way to help him.

The assessment took about three hours, but the time went by really quickly and Sam had lots of breaks, so he could have a drink and relax a bit. Some of the things he had to do started off being really easy but got harder and harder. Mr Burns told Sam not to worry about not being able to do some things because that helped him to understand better how Sam's brain worked. When the assessment was over, Sam wanted to know what Mr Burns had found out. Mr Burns explained that it took him quite a long time to sort out all the results and he would write a report and send it to Kitty and Paul, to Sam's social worker and to the school, in about a week's time.

★

When the report arrived, Sam was eager to find out what it said. Kitty started to read it to him but it had lots of big words he didn't understand. It also had graphs and charts, which Kitty said she didn't understand either, but it did say that Sam was definitely dyslexic and would need lots of help to catch up with the rest of the children in his class. It also said that Sam was really good at some things like art, solving problems and practical jobs like fixing his bike.

The report also described the kind of help Sam would need, like sometimes working one-to-one with a teacher who was specially

★

trained to help children with dyslexia. It also recommended a special programme to use on the computer, and that Sam's teacher should write down what the homework was, so that Sam didn't forget by the time he got home.

There were only two weeks left before the summer holiday started and Kitty told Sam that the help he needed would be sorted out ready for when he went back to school in September.

Sam was so excited. At last he knew for definite that he wasn't "thick". He had a problem he had been born with that would be with him for the rest of his life, but with help and by working hard he could learn to manage it. He could do whatever he wanted to in the future; he could even become famous! He loved living with Kitty and Paul and wanted to stay with them; now it looked like this could really happen.

Rebecca was the best friend he could ever have and he wanted to go to her house to tell her about everything, but Kitty said, 'Hold on

★

Sam, I've got some news for you. Paul and I
have been talking to Rebecca's mum and dad
and because you two get on so well we have
decided that we will go on holiday together. It
will be really good fun.'

'Wow, that's great!' said Sam. 'I can't wait.
Where we are going? Rebecca usually goes all
over the world!'

'What do you mean, all over the world? I don't
think Rebecca has ever been out of this country.'

'Yes she has, she told me. When I first started
talking to her she said she had global something
or other – that means all over the world.'

Kitty thought for a moment, and then started
laughing. 'Oh Sam, I am sorry to disappoint
you. We are going camping in Cornwall.
Rebecca hasn't been all over the world. She
was telling you about her disability; it's called
Global Developmental Delay. She came out of
her mummy's tummy too early and she didn't

★

learn to do things like crawling, talking and feeding herself at the same age as most other children do. When she started school she found it hard to do writing because her muscles don't work properly, and a bit like you, she still finds it hard. I expect you've noticed that she also finds it hard to say some words, and sometimes can't think of the word she needs to use. She still has problems walking, running and riding a bike. Because she is behind with more than two of the things other children don't have a problem with, they call it "global", meaning all over. I am sorry you got confused.'

'Don't worry,' said Sam, 'she's my best friend anyway. I'm going to tell her all about the dyslexia.'

Sam really enjoyed his holiday in Cornwall with Rebecca and her family. They did lots of fun things, even on the days when it was raining. When it was time to go back to school in September, Sam didn't feel worried like he usually did because he knew that he was going to have lots of help for his dyslexia.

★

HALL OF FAME

Can you remember which famous people past or present have dyslexia. Find the clues in the HALL of FAME.

28

Now that you have finished Sam's story there may be lots of questions that you want to ask. If you have been reading this book with an adult, you could go through the questions that come next and talk about them together.

★

Dyslexia

What causes dyslexia?

Some people are born with dyslexia; it can get passed on to them from one of their birth parents – a bit like the colour of your eyes. Some people become dyslexic after an accident or an illness.

Are there more dyslexic boys than girls?

Some studies show that three times as

★

many boys as girls need extra help or teaching because they have dyslexia. But a recent survey has found that there are an equal number of girls and boys with dyslexia.

How many dyslexic people are there?

Roughly 10% of the population of the UK is thought to be dyslexic, with 4% (two-and-a-half million people) being severely affected. It is estimated that there are about 375,000 schoolchildren in the UK with dyslexia.

Can it be cured?

Each dyslexic person's difficulties are different; they can vary from mild to very severe problems. There is no real cure, but children and even grown-ups can be helped by trained teachers who use special learning aids / techniques.

★

Isn't there any medicine that can help you if you have dyslexia?

No, because dyslexia is not an illness.

Does dyslexia only affect reading, writing and spelling?

No, it can affect people in other ways. They may find it hard to organise or to remember things and to use numbers. Some people have more problems with numbers than reading, writing and spelling: this is called dyscalculia and it is less common than dyslexia.

Why is it so important to be able to read and write?

Because it is the most important way to give and receive information. But there are other ways: can you think of any?

Why was Sam embarrassed that he couldn't read or write? It wasn't his fault.

Because it was so hard for him to do what

★

other children could do easily and it made him feel different from everyone else.

Can dyslexia cause other problems?

Some dyslexic children have behavioural problems like temper tantrums or extreme shyness, which may be because they feel confused. These problems usually improve with the right kind of teaching.

Sam was really good at art. What other things are dyslexic people good at?

People with dyslexia can be good at all sorts of things, just like anybody else. Because using a computer can help with reading and writing, some people with dyslexia become computer wizards!

How old do you have to be to find out if you have dyslexia?

Usually, when you go to school and start to learn to read and write, the teacher will notice if you are having problems. If you go

★

on having problems, the teacher will talk to your family or carers about it and you can then be assessed when you are seven or over.

Do you have to have lots of tests to find out if you have dyslexia? Tests can be scary.

You have to have some tests but they are not like exams or spelling tests; they can be fun.

Being dyslexic sounds like it can make life very difficult. How could I help if someone in my class has dyslexia?

You can help by being kind and understanding. Perhaps you could tell them that you have read this book.

Sam was worried that he would have to leave his foster family if they found out that he was "thick". Would foster carers really do that?

No, I'm sure they wouldn't, but children

★

like Sam can feel very confused and worried about being "different". He may even have thought that was the reason for his previous moves in foster care.

Global Developmental Delay

What makes children have Global Developmental Delay?

There are many different reasons for developmental delay. A baby may have been born too early or not have got enough oxygen during birth. Developmental delay might be caused by a childhood illness like meningitis or an accident during childhood. In some cases a baby is just born that way and it is impossible to find out what has caused it.

Is it possible to find out exactly why any one child has developmental delay?

There are lots of different tests that doctors and other experts can use to try and find out. A paediatrician will ask about the

★

child's medical history and examine the child and measure their height, weight and size of their head. They will ask the child's parents or carers how old he or she was when they started to roll over, crawl, walk and talk. They might send the child to see a speech and language therapist, occupational therapist (to find out what the child can and cannot do) or neurologist (a doctor who understands how the brain works).

Knowing what may have caused the developmental delay can help parents and carers to find the best way to look after their child. It can also help everyone to understand what help the child might need at school and in the future.

If you have dyslexia does it mean you also have developmental delay?

No, but some children with developmental delay may also have dyslexia.

Do you get better as you get older? Is there a cure for Global Developmental Delay?

With the right help – though not always – some children may catch up with their friends of the same age. But developmental delay does not stop a child from having a full life with lots of fun.

Why are some children so mean to others just because they are different? In the story Rebecca had never had a best friend until she met Sam. Why did her classmates laugh at her and tease her?

Sometimes children don't understand that everyone is different. They can feel embarrassed or anxious about talking to children who have a disability, just like Sam did. Laughing and teasing isn't a nice thing to do but sometimes children do it to cover up their own feelings and don't think about how sad it makes the other person feel.

★